Science
made easy

Key Stage 1
Ages 5-7 Workbook 3
Finding out Why Things Happen

Author
David Evans

LONDON • NEW YORK • SYDNEY • DELHI • PARIS • MUNICH • JOHANNESBURG

What makes a thing alive?

Science facts

You can tell that something is alive if it moves by itself without being pushed or pulled. Living things eat food. Feeding helps living things to grow. Only living things can produce offspring (reproduce). Living things can use their senses of taste, smell, touch, sight and hearing to react to the world around them.

Science quiz

What is each of these living things doing that tells you it is alive? Use one of the words in the box below to complete each sentence.

reproduces	moves	feeds	reacts	grows

I know this horse is alive because it ....

I know this bird is alive because it ....

I know this boy is alive because he ....

I know this caterpillar is alive because it ....

I know this cat is alive because it ....

Science activity

⚠ Find a snail in a garden or park, and watch it carefully. How can you tell if it is living?

Was a thing ever alive?

Science facts
Living things move, feed, grow, reproduce and react. Living things that can no longer do these things are dead. Some things can never move by themselves, feed, grow, reproduce or react. These things are not alive, and they are called non-living things.

Science quiz
Draw a circle around each thing that is non-living.

Science activity

What can you find out about silk?
Is it a living, a non-living or
a dead material?

Are plants living things?

Science facts

All the living things you have looked at so far have been animals.
Animals move by themselves, grow, feed, react and produce offspring.
Although plants do not move from place to place by themselves or
eat food, they do grow and reproduce. Plants are living things, too.

Science quiz

Draw a line joining each whole plant to the part of it that will grow
into a new plant.

Science activity

 See if you can find a mimosa plant
at a garden centre. What happens
when you touch its leaves? How can
you tell that it is alive?

What keeps things alive?

Science facts

All animals need to eat food and drink water to stay alive. If animals do not eat or drink, they die. Human beings are animals, too, and so need food and water to survive. Some animals eat plants and some eat other animals. Humans eat both plants and animals.

Science quiz

Draw a line joining each animal on the left to the food it eats.

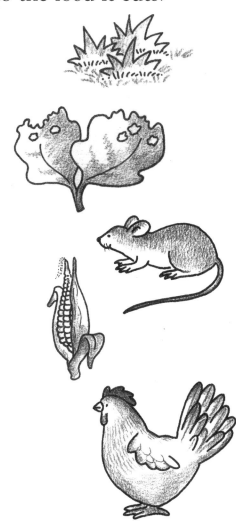

Science activity

Where does the food you eat come from? Make a list of all the animals and plants that you usually eat.

How can you keep healthy?

Science facts

You are a human. You need food and water to stay alive. You also need exercise, which keeps you fit. When your body is healthy, it can move easily. When you exercise hard, your body sweats. Sweat is mainly water. It helps to keep you cool.

Science quiz

Put a tick (✔) by each of the activities that can make you sweat a lot.

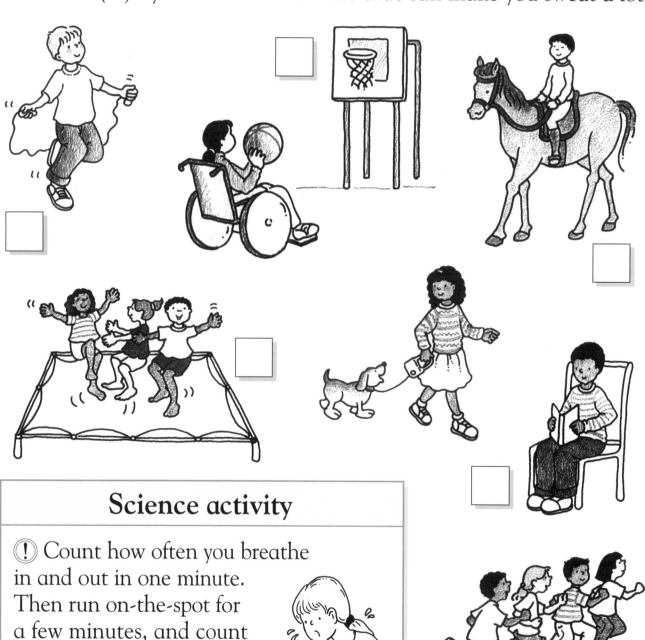

Science activity

(!) Count how often you breathe in and out in one minute. Then run on-the-spot for a few minutes, and count your breaths again. Did you expect these results?

How do we keep teeth healthy?

Science facts

Some of the things you eat and drink, such as milk, help to build strong teeth and bones. However, small bits of food are left on and in-between your teeth when you eat. Sugary foods and drinks can harm your teeth, which then may need to be fixed by a dentist. Brushing your teeth after every meal helps to remove any left-over food. Eating fresh fruit and vegetables also helps clean your teeth.

Science quiz

Which of these foods will help keep your teeth healthy? Colour them in.

Science activity

When you clean your teeth, do you get rid of all the small bits of food? Ask a grown-up to help you use disclosing tablets to find out.

What is healthy eating?

Science facts

Foods such as beans, milk, meat and fish help you grow (these types of food are called proteins). Other foods such as pasta, bread and rice give you energy to work and play (they are called carbohydrates). Foods such as butter and cheese also give you energy (they are called fats). Vitamins and minerals, found in fresh fruit and vegetables, are good for you. Eating the right amounts of each type of food will keep you healthy. Too much fat, salt and sugar could make you ill.

Science quiz

Look at what Justin and Sarah are eating. Who is eating the healthy meal? Cross out (✗) the unhealthy meal. Why do you think it is unhealthy?

Science activity

Look at the labels on boxes and tins of food in your kitchen. How can you find out how much salt there is in each food?

What is a life cycle?

Science facts

Adults produce offspring. Offspring are young animals, which will one day grow into adults themselves. These adults will then produce offspring of their own. This pattern of events is called a life cycle.

Science quiz

Here is the life cycle of a chicken. Which picture goes with which stage in the life cycle? Write **A**, **B**, **C** or **D** in each box?

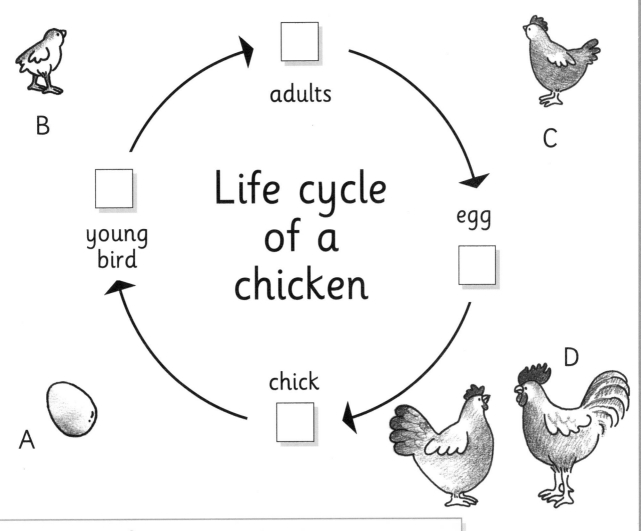

B

adults

young bird

Life cycle of a chicken

egg

C

chick

D

A

Science activity

Find out about stick insects. What are they? Do they have a life cycle? You may need to use reference books, a CD-ROM or the Internet to find out.

How aware are you?

Science facts

Your body reacts to changes in the world around you. Your ears tell you about sounds; your nose tells you about smells; your tongue tells you about tastes; and your eyes tell you about light. When you touch something, your skin can feel if it is rough or smooth, or hot or cold.

Science quiz

How can Sophia sense what is on the table? Draw a line joining each object to the part of her body that can sense it.

Which sense can Sophia not use?

....

Science activity

(!) If you were blindfolded, could you find your way from one side of a room to the other? Try it. Does feeling your way with a stick make it easier?

What helps a plant to grow?

Science facts

Plants do not eat other plants or animals. Instead, they use water and air to make their own food. Plants can only make this food when they grow in sunny places. Plants use their food to grow.

Science quiz

Look at this picture of a garden. The owners have been away on holiday for two weeks.

Why has the grass grown less under the tree than anywhere else?

....

Why do the flowers in the hanging basket look unhealthy?

....

....

Science activity

Grow some cress seeds in a tray. Then, cover half the tray with cardboard for a few days. What happens? Why?

Do plants have life cycles?

Science facts

Many plants have flowers. Flowers make seeds. If a seed lands in soil and gets enough water, it grows into a young plant, called a seedling. The seedling grows into an adult plant with flowers. The flowers produce more seeds. These are stages in a plant's life cycle.

Science quiz

Here is the life cycle of a dandelion. Which picture goes with which stage in the life cycle? Write A, B or C in each box.

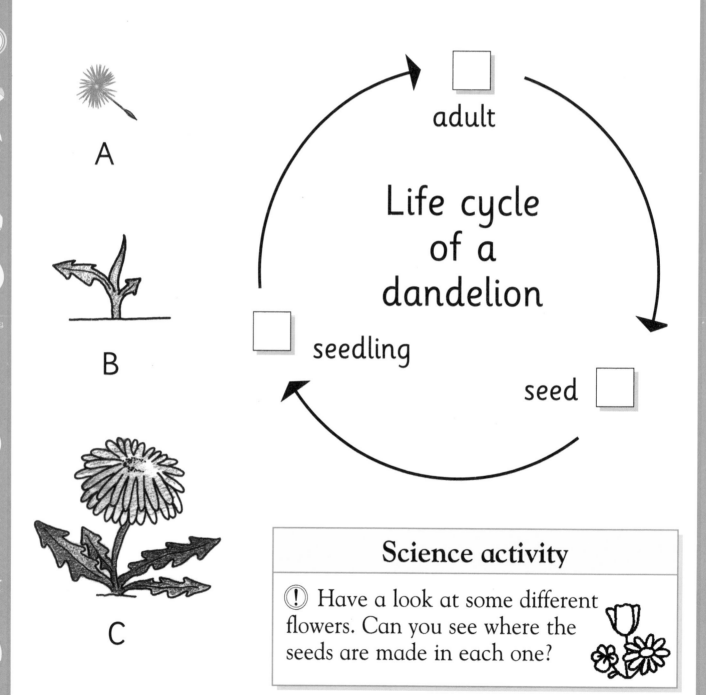

A

B

C

Life cycle
of a
dandelion

adult

seedling

seed

Science activity

⚠ Have a look at some different flowers. Can you see where the seeds are made in each one?

What kind of an animal is it?

Science facts

You can recognise different animal groups by the features they have in common. For example, mammals have hair on their skin; birds have feathers; reptiles have tough scales; amphibians have slimy skin; and fish have thin scales.

Science quiz

Write which group each animal belongs to and what feature it has that tells you so.

 pigeon

A pigeon is a ....

I know because it has ....

A lizard is a ....

I know because it has ....

lizard

 cat

A cat is a ....

I know because it has ....

frog

A frog is an...

I know because it has ....

 goldfish

A goldfish is a ....

I know because it has ....

Science activity

What can you find out about reptiles? Do they all have scales and legs?

What kind of a plant is it?

Science facts

Fruits and vegetables are plants that we eat. Fruits are made by flowers. They usually have seeds inside. Most vegetables are leaves, stems or roots. They do not have seeds.

Science quiz

Can you sort these foods into vegetables and fruits? Write **F** for fruit or **V** for vegetable in the box beside each one.

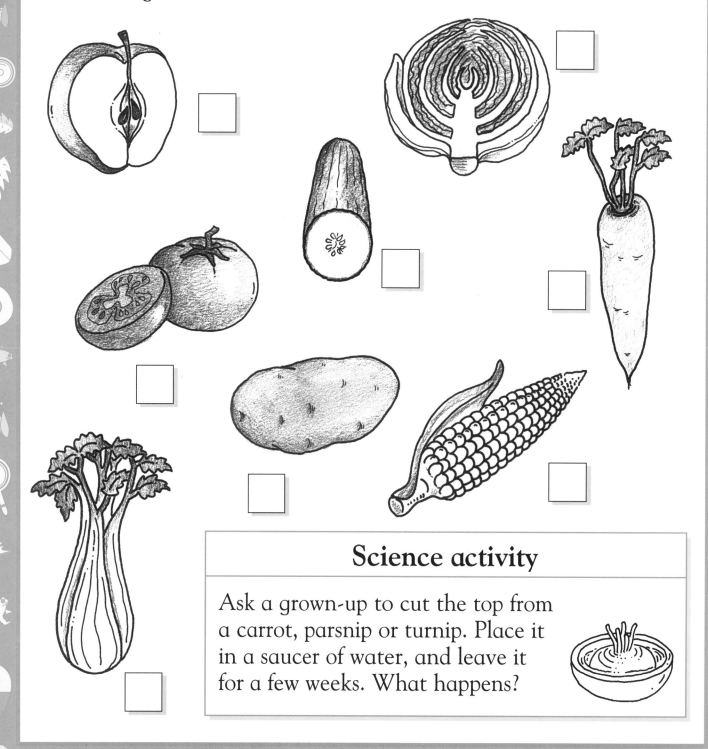

Science activity

Ask a grown-up to cut the top from a carrot, parsnip or turnip. Place it in a saucer of water, and leave it for a few weeks. What happens?

How does that live there?

Science facts

Animals can live on land, in soil, in water and in the air. Some of these places are wet, others are dry. Some are in bright light, others are in the shade. Different animals are adapted to live in different sorts of places.

Science quiz

1 Draw a cross (✗) on one part of the goldfish that helps it live in water.

2 Draw a cross (✗) on one part of the frog that helps it live in water.

3 Draw a tick (✔) on one part of the duck that helps it live in the air, and draw a cross (✗) on a part that helps it live on water.

Science activity

(!) What animals would you expect to find in the darkest parts of a garden or park near where you live? Use a spoon or trowel to find out if you were right. Always wear gloves when you dig in soil.

Is it natural or made in a factory?

Science facts

Natural materials, such as soil, rock and gold, come from the earth. Materials such as plastics and paper are made in factories. Some of the plastics used to make everyday items include: polyester, PVC, polystyrene, polythene and nylon.

Science quiz

Can you unscramble the groups of jumbled-up letters below to spell the names of different plastics? Fill in the missing letters in the blank spaces.

opelsyrenty

1 __ o __ y __ t __ r __ n __ is used to make drinking cups.

VPC

2 __ V __ is used to make garden hose pipes.

thenopyle

3 P __ l __ t __ e __ e is used to make food bags.

lonny

4 N __ __ __ n is used to make pairs of tights.

lotseprey

5 P __ l __ e __ t __ r is used to make fabrics.

Science activity

What can you find out about glass? Is it found naturally or is it made in a factory? Use reference books, CD-ROMs or the Internet to find out.

Answer Section with Parents' Notes

Key Stage 1 Ages 5–7 Finding out why things happen

This section provides explanatory notes and answers to all the *Science quizzes*. Read through each page together, and ensure that your child understands each task. Point out any mistakes in your child's work, and correct any errors, but also remember to praise your child's efforts and achievements. Where appropriate, ask your child to predict the outcome of the *Science activities*. After each activity, challenge your child to explain his or her results.

When handling soil, make sure that gloves are worn and that hands are washed afterwards. Gloves are also advisable for freezer activities, as very cold objects can "burn" the skin.

---

2 ☆ What makes a thing alive?

Science facts
You can tell that something is alive if it moves by itself without being pushed or pulled. Living things eat food. Feeding helps living things to grow. Only living things can produce offspring (reproduce). Living things can use their senses of taste, smell, touch, sight and hearing to react to the world around them.

Science quiz
What is each of these living things doing that tells you it is alive? Use one of the words in the box below to complete each sentence.

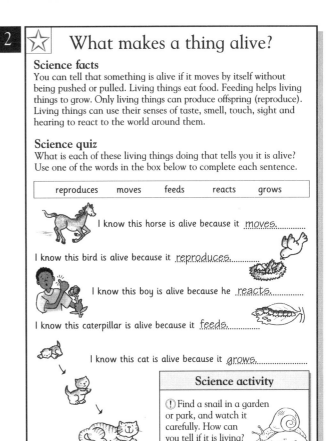

| reproduces | moves | feeds | reacts | grows |

I know this horse is alive because it _moves_.

I know this bird is alive because it _reproduces_.

I know this boy is alive because he _reacts_.

I know this caterpillar is alive because it _feeds_.

I know this cat is alive because it _grows_.

> **Science activity**
> ⚠ Find a snail in a garden or park, and watch it carefully. How can you tell if it is living?

On this page, your child learns that living things move, eat, grow, sense things and reproduce. When your child finds a snail, draw his or her attention to the snail's eye stalks and antennae, which will show clearly that it reacts to stimuli.

---

3 Was a thing ever alive? ☆

Science facts
Living things move, feed, grow, reproduce and react. Living things that can no longer do these things are dead. Some things can never move by themselves, feed, grow, reproduce or react. These things are not alive, and they are called non-living things.

Science quiz
Draw a circle around each thing that is non-living.

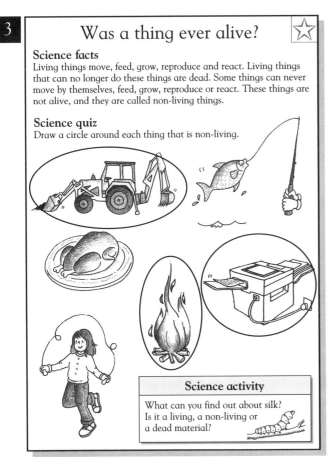

> **Science activity**
> What can you find out about silk? Is it a living, a non-living or a dead material?

Here, your child finds out about dead and non-living things. Find some silk for your child to look at, and help him or her to discover that it is woven. You could look up silk in an encyclopedia or on a CD-ROM to find out where it comes from.

---

4 ☆ Are plants living things?

Science facts
All the living things you have looked at so far have been animals. Animals move by themselves, grow, feed, react and produce offspring. Although plants do not move from place to place by themselves or eat food, they do grow and reproduce. Plants are living things, too.

Science quiz
Draw a line joining each whole plant to the part of it that will grow into a new plant.

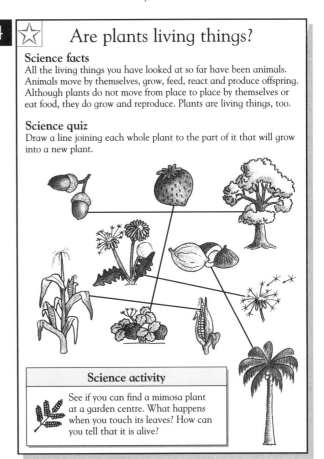

> **Science activity**
> See if you can find a mimosa plant at a garden centre. What happens when you touch its leaves? How can you tell that it is alive?

Children often find it hard to understand that plants are living things, because they cannot see them moving. The best evidence that plants are alive is that they grow and reproduce. Give your child every opportunity to observe these things.

5   What keeps things alive?

Science facts
All animals need to eat food and drink water to stay alive. If animals do not eat or drink, they die. Human beings are animals, too, and so need food and water to survive. Some animals eat plants and some eat other animals. Humans eat both plants and animals.

Science quiz
Draw a line joining each animal on the left to the food it eats.

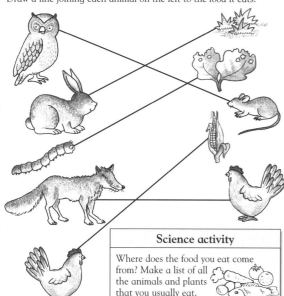

Science activity
Where does the food you eat come from? Make a list of all the animals and plants that you usually eat.

Animals need food and water to stay alive. If you have a pet, involve your child when it is fed. Help your child work out which of the foods you eat are of plant origin and which are of animal origin, perhaps by looking at the ingredients on packets.

---

6   How can you keep healthy?

Science facts
You are a human. You need food and water to stay alive. You also need exercise, which keeps you fit. When your body is healthy, it can move easily. When you exercise hard, your body sweats. Sweat is mainly water. It helps to keep you cool.

Science quiz
Put a tick (✔) by each of the activities that can make you sweat a lot.

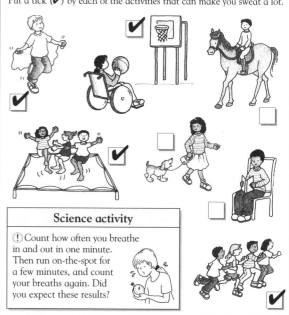

Science activity
⚠ Count how often you breathe in and out in one minute. Then run on-the-spot for a few minutes, and count your breaths again. Did you expect these results?

This page focuses on the importance of exercise. Encourage your child to predict the results of the experiment. Afterwards, ask whether what happened is what he or she predicted. Supervise the activity if your child has asthma.

---

7   How do we keep teeth healthy? ☆

Science facts
Some of the things you eat and drink, such as milk, help to build strong teeth and bones. However, small bits of food are left on and in-between your teeth when you eat. Sugary foods and drinks can harm your teeth, which then may need to be fixed by a dentist. Brushing your teeth after every meal helps to remove any left-over bits of food. Eating crunchy fresh fruit also helps clean your teeth.

Science quiz
Which of these foods will help keep your teeth healthy? Colour them in.

Science activity
When you clean your teeth, do you get rid of all the small bits of food? Ask a grown-up to help you use disclosing tablets to find out.

These activities teach your child that eating the right food helps to keep teeth healthy. Remember to praise your child for correct answers in the quiz. You can buy disclosing tablets or liquid for the experiment from most chemists or dentists.

---

8   What is healthy eating? ☆

Science facts
Foods such as beans, milk, meat and fish help you grow (these types of food are called proteins). Other foods such as pasta, bread and rice give you energy to work and play (they are called carbohydrates). Foods such as butter and cheese also give you energy (they are called fats). Vitamins and minerals, found in fresh fruit and vegetables, are good for you. Eating the right amounts of each type of food will keep you healthy. Too much fat, salt and sugar could make you ill.

Science quiz
Look at what Justin and Sarah are eating. Who is eating the healthy meal? Cross out (✘) the unhealthy meal. Why do you think it is unhealthy?

Science activity
Look at the labels on boxes and tins of food in your kitchen. How can you find out how much salt there is in each food?

This page helps your child to recognise the importance of a healthy diet. Most food packaging has a chart showing the food content, including salt. Explain to your child that too much salt can lead to heart problems later in life.

What is a life cycle?

Science facts
Adults produce offspring. Offspring are young animals, which will one day grow into adults themselves. These adults will then produce offspring of their own. This pattern of events is called a life cycle.

Science quiz
Here is the life cycle of a chicken. Which picture goes with which stage in the life cycle? Write **A**, **B**, **C** or **D** in each box?

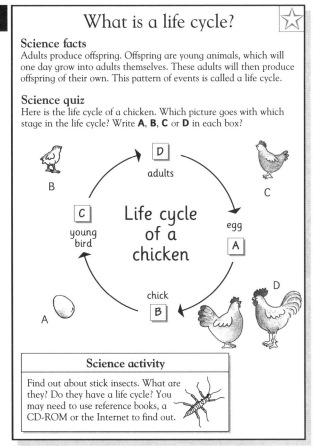

Life cycle of a chicken

adults D

egg A

chick B

young bird C

B   C   A   D

Science activity
Find out about stick insects. What are they? Do they have a life cycle? You may need to use reference books, a CD-ROM or the Internet to find out.

This page introduces the idea that all animals go through a life cycle. Rearing stick insects at home is a good way for your child to observe a life cycle at first hand. Alternatively, a good reference book or CD-ROM will show various animals' life cycles.

How aware are you?

Science facts
Your body reacts to changes in the world around you. Your ears tell you about sounds; your nose tells you about smells; your tongue tells you about tastes; and your eyes tell you about light. When you touch something, your skin can feel if it is rough or smooth, or hot or cold.

Science quiz
How can Sophia sense what is on the table? Draw a line joining each object to the part of her body that can sense it.

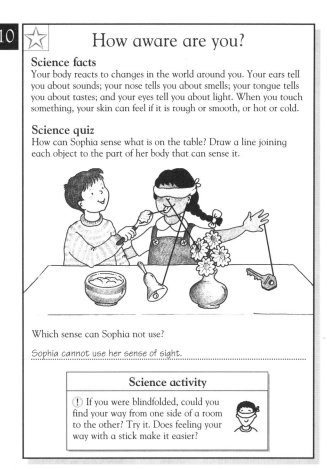

Which sense can Sophia not use?

Sophia cannot use her sense of sight.

Science activity
⚠ If you were blindfolded, could you find your way from one side of a room to the other? Try it. Does feeling your way with a stick make it easier?

Here, your child learns that special organs are used to sense changes in the environment. The experiment will help your child become aware of how much he or she relies on sight and also help him or her understand what it means to be blind.

What helps a plant to grow?

Science facts
Plants do not eat other plants or animals. Instead, they use water and air to make their own food. Plants can only make this food when they grow in sunny places. Plants use their food to grow.

Science quiz
Look at this picture of a garden. The owners have been away on holiday for two weeks.

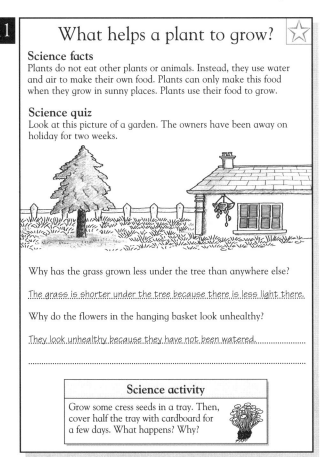

Why has the grass grown less under the tree than anywhere else?

The grass is shorter under the tree because there is less light there.

Why do the flowers in the hanging basket look unhealthy?

They look unhealthy because they have not been watered.

Science activity
Grow some cress seeds in a tray. Then, cover half the tray with cardboard for a few days. What happens? Why?

On this page, your child discovers that plants require water and light to grow. In the quiz, you are looking for answers that contain "because" statements: for example, "The grass is shorter under the tree because there is less light there."

Do plants have life cycles?

Science facts
Many plants have flowers. Flowers make seeds. If a seed lands in soil and gets enough water, it grows into a young plant, called a seedling. The seedling grows into an adult plant with flowers. The flowers produce more seeds. These are stages in a plant's life cycle.

Science quiz
Here is the life cycle of a dandelion. Which picture goes with which stage in the life cycle? Write A, B or C in each box.

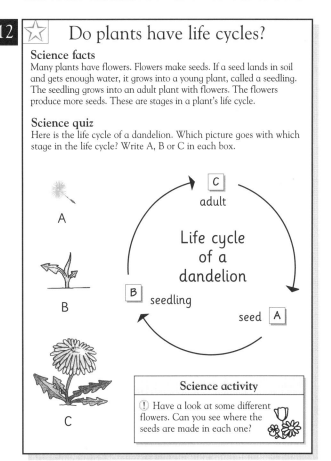

Life cycle of a dandelion

adult C

seed A

seedling B

A   B   C

Science activity
⚠ Have a look at some different flowers. Can you see where the seeds are made in each one?

This page focuses on plant life cycles. Watch out for flowers from poisonous plants, such as nightshades. If your child has hay fever or asthma, supervise this experiment closely. Seeds are often easiest to find in autumn.

What kind of an animal is it?

Science facts
You can recognise different animal groups by the features they have in common. For example, mammals have hair on their skin; birds have feathers; reptiles have tough scales; amphibians have slimy skin; and fish have thin scales.

Science quiz
Write which group each animal belongs to and what feature it has that tells you so.

 pigeon

A pigeon is a <u>bird</u>.

I know because it has <u>feathers</u>

 lizard

A lizard is a <u>reptile</u>.

I know because it has <u>tough scales</u>.

cat

A cat is a <u>mammal</u>.

I know because it has <u>hair</u>.

 frog

A frog is an <u>amphibian</u>.

I know because it has <u>slimy skin</u>.

goldfish

A goldfish is a <u>fish</u>.

I know because it has <u>thin scales</u>.

Science activity
What can you find out about reptiles? Do they all have scales and legs?

These activities teach your child how to group animals according to shared features. Ask your child which group humans belong to. Your child could find out about reptiles at a zoo or by using a reference book or CD-ROM at the library.

☆ What kind of a plant is it?

Science facts
Fruits and vegetables are plants that we eat. Fruits are made by flowers. They usually have seeds inside. Most vegetables are leaves, stems or roots. They do not have seeds.

Science quiz
Can you sort these foods into vegetables and fruits? Write **F** for fruit or **V** for vegetable in the box beside each one.

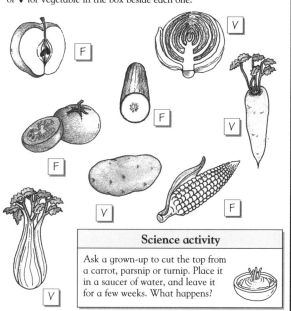

 F

V

F

F

V

F

V

V

Science activity
Ask a grown-up to cut the top from a carrot, parsnip or turnip. Place it in a saucer of water, and leave it for a few weeks. What happens?

This page focuses on plants and how they can be grouped by shared features. The aim of the quiz is for your child to use his or her knowledge of the features of fruit and vegetables to classify each plant. Remember to praise all correct answers.

How does that live there? ☆

Science facts
Animals can live on land, in soil, in water and in the air. Some of these places are wet, others are dry. Some are in bright light, others are in the shade. Different animals are adapted to live in different sorts of places.

Answers may vary

Science quiz

1 Draw a cross (✗) on one part of the goldfish that helps it live in water.

2 Draw a cross (✗) on one part of the frog that helps it live in water.

3 Draw a tick (✔) on one part of the duck that helps it live in the air, and draw a cross (✗) on a part that helps it live on water.

Science activity
(!) What animals would you expect to find in the darkest parts of a garden or park near where you live? Use a spoon or trowel to find out if you were right. Always wear gloves when you dig in soil.

The theme on this page is habitats and how each animal is adapted to its own. Supervise the experiment, and ensure that your child wears gloves when touching soil. Encourage your child to predict what animals he or she might find.

☆ Is it natural or made in a factory?

Science facts
Natural materials, such as soil, rock and gold, come from the earth. Materials such as plastics and paper are made in factories. Some of the plastics used to make everyday items include: polyester, PVC, polystyrene, polythene and nylon.

Science quiz
Can you unscramble the groups of jumbled-up letters below to spell the names of different plastics? Fill in the missing letters in the blank spaces.

opelsyrenty

1 <u>P o l y s t y r e n e</u> is used to make drinking cups.

VPC

2 <u>P V C</u> is used to make garden hose pipes.

thenopyle

3 <u>P o l y t h e n e</u> is used to make food bags.

lonny

4 <u>N y l o n</u> is used to make pairs of tights.

lotseprey

5 <u>P o l y e s t e r</u> is used to make fabrics.

Science activity
What can you find out about glass? Is it found naturally or is it made in a factory? Use reference books, CD-ROMs or the Internet to find out.

Here, your child discovers that some materials are natural and others are manufactured. Help your child to look up glass in a reference book or CD-ROM. Point out that many factory-produced materials use natural "ingredients", such as sand.

Why do we use that material?

Science facts

When a house is built, materials such as wood, metal, plastic and ceramic are used. Each material is chosen because it does a particular job well. For example, clay is used to make bricks because baked clay is strong and does not let water through quickly.

Science quiz

Draw a line joining each sentence on the left to the words on the right that describe that material's use.

Wood planks make good floors — because it lets light through.

Glass is used to glaze windows — because it does not rot.

Metal girders are used in buildings — because they're flat and smooth.

Clay is used to make roof tiles — because they're very strong.

Plastic is used for window frames — because it's waterproof.

Science activity

Which type of paper – newspaper, wallpaper, tissue paper or crepe paper – is best for wrapping a small parcel to send through the post? Think up some experiments to find out. Try them out.

Here, your child learns that different properties make materials suitable for different purposes. Help your child to decide what qualities wrapping paper requires (e.g., strength and flexibility) and to devise tests to see which paper is most suitable.

Which is the best material to use?

Science facts

When you make something, it is important to use materials that are right for the job. You would not make a bicycle out of tissue paper or a book out of metal. The owners of factories that make new things ask scientists to carry out tests to find the best materials to use.

Science quiz

A factory owner wanted to know which fabric she should use to make swimming costumes that dry quickly. She asked a scientist to do a test. He made four costumes of the same size from different materials, then rinsed them in water and left them to dry. Here are his results.

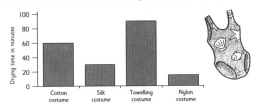

1 Which material should she choose? _nylon_

2 Why is that the best choice? _Nylon dries the quickest._

3 Why did the scientist make all the costumes the same size?
   They were made the same size to make the test fair.

Science activity

Which material – cotton, paper, aluminium foil or vinyl – would be best for making an easy-to-clean painting apron? Design your own experiment to find out. How will you keep your experiment fair?

This page offers further practice in choosing suitable materials for a purpose. Interpreting information from a chart or graph is an important skill. Encourage your child to look at charts whenever possible and to say what they show.

Which metals are attracted?

Science facts

Magnets are usually made of the metals iron, steel or cobalt. When a magnet is held near an object made of the metals iron or steel, the the magnet pulls the object towards itself.

Science quiz

Steve said that magnets attract all metals. Rachel said that magnets attract some metals, but not all. They did an experiment to find out who was right. Colour in each of the metal items that you think will be attracted to the magnet.

cast-iron saucepan

brass key

lead pencil

steel spoon

copper kettle

aluminium can

Who was right, Steve or Rachel? _Rachel_

Science activity

Rub a metal paper clip against a magnet for one minute. Then try using the paper clip to attract another paper clip. What happens?

The theme on this page is magnetism. Before starting the experiment, ask your child to test whether the paper clip is already a magnet – see whether it attracts other paper clips. Afterwards, try the same test again.

Will it stretch?

Science facts

Elastic materials stretch when you pull them. When you stop pulling, they go back to the size they were. Elastic materials also squash when you squeeze them. When you stop squeezing, they go back to the shape they were.

Science quiz

Cora wanted to find out how elastic bands stretched. She tied three plastic pots to elastic bands and hung the pots from a rail. Then she put three glass marbles into the first pot, four into the second and five into the third. Here are the results of her experiment.

1 What happens to each elastic band as more marbles are put in the pot below it?

   The more marbles you add, the more the band stretches.

2 Draw a fourth pot hanging from the rail. It should show what would happen if six marbles were put into the pot.

Science activity

What happens if you stand a plastic pot on a bath sponge and then add marbles to the pot one by one?

These activities show that elastic materials can be stretched or squashed. You could extend the quiz by doing the experiment yourselves. Try different materials, such as string, spaghetti or wire, to see whether all materials stretch and are elastic.

Is it waterproof?

Science facts
When you pour water on some materials, such as net-curtain fabric, the water passes straight through. Other materials, such as polythene, do not let water through. They are called waterproof materials.

Science quiz
Sunil wanted to know why different fabrics are used to make different clothes. He did an experiment to find out which fabric is best for making raincoats. He took pieces of different fabrics and poured a large spoonful of water over each one in turn. Here are his results.

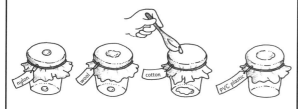

Which fabric is best for making raincoats?

PVC plastic is the best fabric for making raincoats.

Why is this fabric best?

This fabric is best because no water passes through it.

Science activity
(!) Gloves made from which material keep your hands warmest? To find out, put on different types of gloves and pick up a bag of ice cubes.

Here, your child looks at waterproof materials. Provide as many different gloves as possible for the experiment – leather, wool, rubber, cotton and oven gloves. Ask your child which gloves are best at preventing the cold of the ice being felt.

Will it ever change back?

Science facts
When ice cream melts, you can make it hard again by cooling it in a freezer. You can make frozen ice cream soft by heating it up. These changes can be changed back (reversed). When a match burns, it changes into ash and smoke. You cannot change the ash and smoke back into a match. This change cannot be reversed.

Science quiz
For each of the changes described below, draw a circle around the **H** if the change can be reversed by heating, around the **C** if the change can be reversed by cooling, and around the **N** if it can never be reversed.

Charcoal is burned on a barbecue — H, C or (N)?

Water turns to steam in a kettle — H, (C) or N?

Flour, eggs, sugar and butter are made into a cake — H, C or (N)?

Butter becomes soft in the dish — H, (C) or N?

Bread is made into toast — H, C or (N)?

Water turns to ice in the freezer — (H) C or N?

Chocolate melts and becomes runny — H, (C) or N?

Science activity
How long do you think hair with gel in it will stand up? Put some gel in your hair, and ask a grown-up to time how long it takes for your hair to droop.

Here, your child learns that only some changes are reversible. In the quiz, ask your child to explain his or her choices using the word *because*. If your child suffers from allergies, use hair gel without perfume or colouring for the experiment.

Can electricity be dangerous?

Science facts
To use a hair drier, you must first plug it into a wall socket. Electricity from the socket makes the drier work. You must be very careful when plugging things into a socket. Never touch the metal pins at the end of a plug, and never touch anything electrical with wet hands, because you could get an electric shock – an electric shock can hurt or even kill you. You must also be careful with electricity as it can cause fires.

Science quiz
Write **yes** or **no** to answer each of these questions.

1 Can electricity give you a shock? — yes

2 Can electricity kill you? — yes

3 Can electricity cause a fire? — yes

4 Should you always use batteries for your experiments at home? — yes

5 Should you ever play with electric plugs or wall sockets? — no

6 Should you put wires into electrical wall sockets? — no

7 Should you use plugs and wall sockets for experiments at home? — no

8 Should you always ask an adult before plugging something into a wall socket? — yes

Science activity
(!) Where are the electrical sockets in your home? What sorts of things need to be plugged in before they work?

These activities teach your child about the dangers of mains electricity. This is a good opportunity to teach your child never to experiment with mains electricity, never to pull out a plug by the cable and never to touch a plug with wet hands.

Will the bulb light up?

Science facts
To light up a bulb with a battery, you need to make a circuit. All the parts of the circuit must be connected in the right order for the bulb to light up. This is called making a complete circuit.

Science quiz
Sunil, Claire, Sean and Lata each tried to make a bulb light up using a battery and wires. Who made the bulb light up? Tick (✔) the right box.

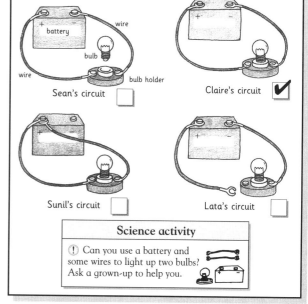

Sean's circuit [ ]   Claire's circuit [✔]

Sunil's circuit [ ]   Lata's circuit [ ]

Science activity
(!) Can you use a battery and some wires to light up two bulbs? Ask a grown-up to help you.

Here, your child discovers that an electrical device will only work when there is a complete circuit. In the activity, help your child to find the right places to attach the wires to the battery and two bulbs.

How are things turned off or on?

Science facts
If you put a switch into a circuit, you can turn a bulb, a motor or a buzzer on or off. When a switch is turned off, it breaks the circuit. When a switch is turned on, it completes the circuit. Things such as bulbs, motors and buzzers only work when a circuit is complete.

This is an open switch.
It is turned off.

This is a closed switch.
It is turned on.

Science quiz
Which of the circuits shown below will let the buzzer, bulb or motor work? Tick (✔) the right box.

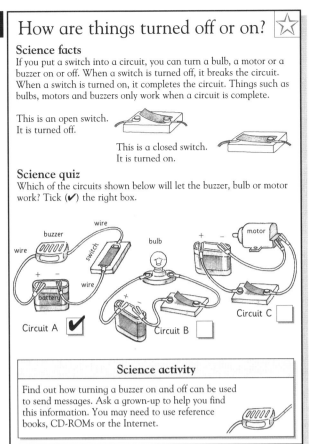

Science activity
Find out how turning a buzzer on and off can be used to send messages. Ask a grown-up to help you find this information. You may need to use reference books, CD-ROMs or the Internet.

This page focuses on switches. Your child could make a simple switch from two drawing pins and a paper clip mounted on thick card, then use it to control a circuit. Help your child to look up Samuel Morse and his code in a reference book.

How do things start and stop?

Science facts
Pushes and pulls are forces. When you push or pull something, you can make it start or stop moving.

Science quiz
Look at these pictures. Is the child in each one using a pushing force or a pulling force? Write **push** or **pull**. Does the force make a start or a stop? Write **start** or **stop**.

....pull........
....stop......

....push......
....start.....

....push.....
....start.....

....pull......
....start.....

....push.....
....stop......

Science activity
Using a rope, play a game of tug of war with a friend. Can you make your friend start moving? Can you make your friend stop moving?

Here, your child learns that forces make objects start and stop moving. Playing tug of war, your child will feel a pulling force at work. Supervise the game, and ask, "Who is pulling the hardest?", "Who is moving?" and "Who is stopping?"

What makes things go faster?

Science facts
Pushes and pulls are forces that can make things move faster or slower. Pushes and pulls can also make things stop moving.

Science quiz
Can you answer these questions about making things move faster or slower?

How can Jason make the ball roll slower?

He can make the slope less steep.................

How can Amy make the ball move faster?

She can kick the ball harder...........................

How can Luke make the bike go slower?

He can push the pedals more slowly.......

How can Anna make the ball move faster?

She can hit the ball harder with the bat.

Science activity
Roll a marble through a cardboard tube. How can you use the tube to make the marble roll faster? How can you use it to make the marble roll slower?

These activities show that a force can make an object speed up or slow down. Talk about gravity, a force that pulls things downwards. It is gravity that pulls the marble down the slope – the steeper the slope, the faster it moves.

Why do things change direction?

Science facts
Pushes and pulls are forces. Forces can make moving things change direction. If you blow at a table tennis ball that is rolling towards you, the ball will change direction. When you blow, your breath is the force pushing the ball.

Science quiz
Write **yes** or **no** beside each picture below to say whether or not the player is using a force that will make the ball change direction.

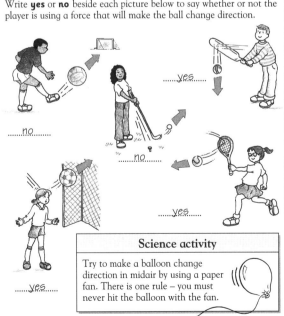

.......yes.......

.......no.......

.......no.......

.......yes.......

.......yes......

Science activity
Try to make a balloon change direction in midair by using a paper fan. There is one rule – you must never hit the balloon with the fan.

On this page, your child learns that a force can make a moving object change direction. Extend the experiment by using fans of different sizes. Your child could also prove this by using a straw to blow (push) and suck (pull) a table-tennis ball.

What makes a shadow?

Science facts

Light comes from different sources, such as the Sun, light bulbs and candles. When light shines on a wall, the ground or a piece of paper, it makes that thing look bright. When no light is shining, everything looks dark. By putting your hand between a light source and a surface, you can make a shadow. A shadow is a place where no light is shining.

Science quiz

Can you add the girl's shadow to this picture? Make sure it is in the right position.

Science activity

(!) Cut some shapes of people and animals out of cardboard. In a dark room, use your shapes and a torch to make a shadow-puppet show. What happens if you cut out the shapes from clear cling film?

The theme of this page is shadows. If an object is placed between a light and a surface, light cannot pass through the object, and so a shadow is formed. Transparent objects (such as cling film) let most of the light through, so only a pale shadow is formed.

What makes the sound change?

Science facts

A sound on a guitar is made by plucking a string. You can change the sound by changing the length of the string. Long strings make low notes; short strings make high notes. Other musical instruments work in similar ways.

Science quiz

Here are the wooden bars of a xylophone that has been taken apart. Number them in order from the lowest note to the highest note. Write **1** in the box below the lowest note and **8** below the highest.

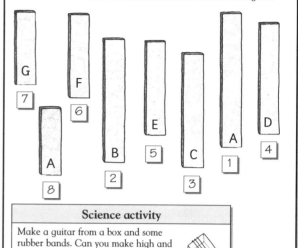

Science activity

Make a guitar from a box and some rubber bands. Can you make high and low sounds on your guitar? Can you make loud and soft sounds?

The quiz requires your child to understand how a guitar's pitch can be altered and then to apply the principle to a xylophone. Your child will need to use a ruler to find the answer. Encourage your child to explore the pitch and loudness of other instruments.

Can you hear it from far away?

Science facts

You use your ears to hear sounds. When a sound is near you, it can sound loud. When the same sound is far away, it will sound quieter.

Science quiz

Look at this picture. Sam is calling her friends to come inside and eat.

Which friend finds it the easiest to hear Sam calling?
Gemma

Which friend finds it the hardest to hear her calling?
Maisy

How can Sam make sure all her friends hear?
Sam should call out louder.

Science activity

Do you think it would be easier to hear quiet sounds if you had bigger ears? Ask a grown-up to help you make a cone from thin card. Hold the tapered end of the cone to your ear, and listen to faraway sounds. Do sounds seem louder with or without the cone?

On this page, your child learns that when a sound is far away, it is quieter. To make the experiment fair, use the same sound, first with "normal" ears and then with the cone ("ear extension") made from thin card.

What do these words mean?

Science facts

Scientists use special words. These words help them to write scientific information for others to read.

Science quiz

Can you remember what these words mean? Draw a line to join each scientific word with the phrase that describes it.

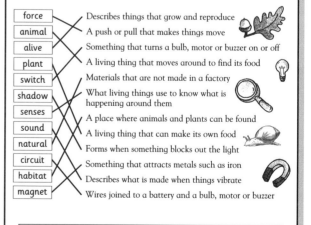

force	Describes things that grow and reproduce
animal	A push or pull that makes things move
alive	Something that turns a bulb, motor or buzzer on or off
plant	A living thing that moves around to find its food
switch	Materials that are not made in a factory
shadow	What living things use to know what is happening around them
senses	A place where animals and plants can be found
sound	A living thing that can make its own food
natural	Forms when something blocks out the light
circuit	Something that attracts metals such as iron
habitat	Describes what is made when things vibrate
magnet	Wires joined to a battery and a bulb, motor or buzzer

Science activity

Think about all the experiments and activities you carried out. How many times did you predict the correct answer? Were all the tests fair? If you repeated the experiments, would you do any of them differently?

This page revises the meanings of some scientific terms used in the book. If necessary, help your child to refer back to the relevant sections of the book to look for the answers. Help your child to reflect on the experiments he or she carried out.

Why do we use that material?

Science facts

When a house is built, materials such as wood, metal, plastic and ceramic are used. Each material is chosen because it does a particular job well. For example, clay is used to make bricks because baked clay is strong and does not let water through quickly.

Science quiz

Draw a line joining each sentence on the left to the words on the right that describe that material's use.

Wood planks make good floors   because it lets light through.

Glass is used to glaze windows   because it does not rot.

Metal girders are used in buildings   because they're flat and smooth.

Clay is used to make roof tiles   because they're very strong.

Plastic is used for window frames   because it's waterproof.

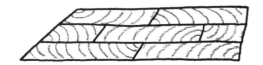

Science activity

Which type of paper – newspaper, wallpaper, tissue paper or crepe paper – is best for wrapping a small parcel to send through the post? Think up some experiments to find out. Try them out.

Which is the best material to use?

Science facts

When you make something, it is important to use materials that are right for the job. You would not make a bicycle out of tissue paper or a book out of metal. The owners of factories that make new things ask scientists to carry out tests to find the best materials to use.

Science quiz

A factory owner wanted to know which fabric she should use to make swimming costumes that dry quickly. She asked a scientist to do a test. He made four costumes of the same size from different materials, then rinsed them in water and left them to dry. Here are his results.

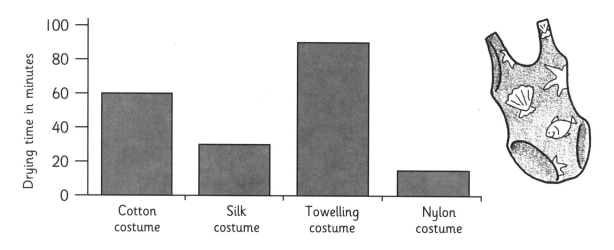

1   Which material should she choose? ....

2   Why is that the best choice? ....

3   Why did the scientist make all the costumes the same size?

....

Science activity

Which material – cotton, paper, aluminium foil or vinyl – would be best for making an easy-to-clean painting apron? Design your own experiment to find out. How will you keep your experiment fair?

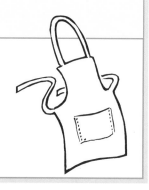

Which metals are attracted?

Science facts

Magnets are usually made of the metals iron, steel or cobalt. When a magnet is held near an object made of the metals iron or steel, the the magnet pulls the object towards itself.

Science quiz

Steve said that magnets attract all metals. Rachel said that magnets attract some metals, but not all. They did an experiment to find out who was right. Colour in each of the metal items that you think will be attracted to the magnet.

cast-iron saucepan

brass key

lead pencil

steel spoon

copper kettle

aluminium can

Who was right, Steve or Rachel? ....

Science activity

Stroke a metal paper clip along a magnet, in one direction only, for one minute. Then try using the clip to attract another clip.

Will it stretch?

Science facts

Elastic materials stretch when you pull them. When you stop pulling, they go back to the size they were. Elastic materials also squash when you squeeze them. When you stop squeezing, they go back to the shape they were.

Science quiz

Cora wanted to find out how elastic bands stretched. She tied three plastic pots to elastic bands and hung the pots from a rail. Then she put three glass marbles into the first pot, four into the second and five into the third. Here are the results of her experiment.

1   What happens to each elastic band as more marbles are put in the pot below it?

2   Draw a fourth pot hanging from the rail. It should show what would happen if six marbles were put into the pot.

Science activity

What happens if you stand a plastic pot on a bath sponge and then add marbles to the pot one by one?

Is it waterproof?

Science facts

When you pour water on some materials, such as net-curtain fabric, the water passes straight through. Other materials, such as polythene, do not let water through. They are called waterproof materials.

Science quiz

Sunil wanted to know why different fabrics are used to make different clothes. He did an experiment to find out which fabric is best for making raincoats. He took pieces of different fabrics and poured a large spoonful of water over each one in turn. Here are his results.

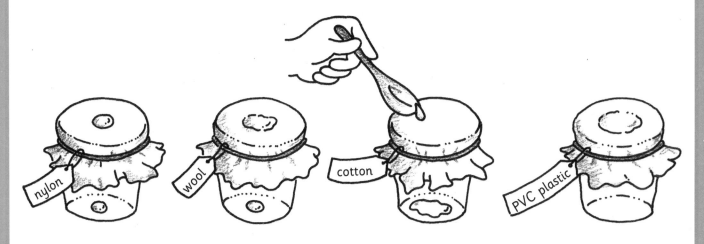

Which fabric is best for making raincoats?

....

Why is this fabric best?

....

Science activity

⚠ Gloves made from which material keep your hands warmest? To find out, put on different types of gloves and pick up a bag of ice cubes.

Will it ever change back?

Science facts

When ice cream melts, you can make it hard again by cooling it in a freezer. You can make frozen ice cream soft by heating it up. These changes can be changed back (reversed). When a match burns, it changes into ash and smoke. You cannot change the ash and smoke back into a match. This change cannot be reversed.

Science quiz

For each of the changes described below, draw a circle around the **H** if the change can be reversed by heating, around the **C** if the change can be reversed by cooling, and around the **N** if it can never be reversed.

Charcoal is burned on a barbecue	H, C or N?
Water turns to steam in a kettle	H, C or N?
Flour, eggs, sugar and butter are made into a cake	H, C or N?
Butter becomes soft in the dish	H, C or N?
Bread is made into toast	H, C or N?
Water turns to ice in the freezer	H, C or N?
Chocolate melts and becomes runny	H, C or N?

Science activity

How long do you think hair with gel in it will stand up? Put some gel in your hair, and ask a grown-up to time how long it takes for your hair to droop.

Can electricity be dangerous?

Science facts

To use a hair dryer, you must first plug it into a wall socket. Electricity from the socket makes the dryer work. You must be very careful when plugging things into a socket. Never touch the metal pins at the end of a plug, and never touch anything electrical with wet hands, because you could get an electric shock – an electric shock can hurt or even kill you. You must also be careful with electricity as it can cause fires.

Science quiz

Write **yes** or **no** to answer each of these questions.

1   Can electricity give you a shock? ....

2   Can electricity kill you? ....

3   Can electricity cause a fire? ....

4   Should you always use batteries for your experiments
    at home? ....

5   Should you ever play with electric plugs or wall sockets? ....

6   Should you put wires into electrical wall sockets? ....

7   Should you use plugs and wall sockets for experiments
    at home? ....

8   Should you always ask an adult before plugging
    something into a wall socket? ....

Science activity

(!) Where are the electrical sockets in your home? What sorts of things need to be plugged in before they work?

Will the bulb light up?

Science facts

To light up a bulb with a battery, you need to make a circuit.
All the parts of the circuit must be connected in the right order for
the bulb to light up. This is called making a complete circuit.

Science quiz

Sunil, Claire, Sean and Lata each tried to make a bulb light up
using a battery and wires. Who made the bulb light up? Tick (✔)
the right box.

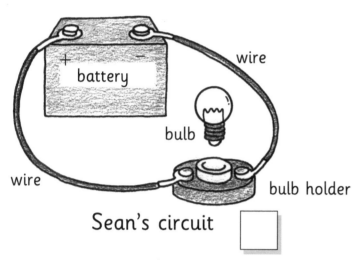

wire

battery

bulb

wire

bulb holder

Sean's circuit ☐

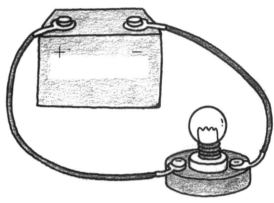

Claire's circuit ☐

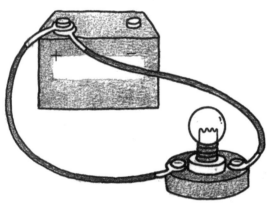

Sunil's circuit ☐

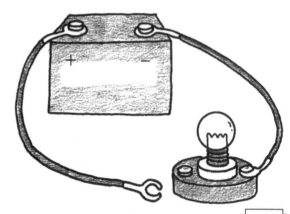

Lata's circuit ☐

Science activity

ⓘ Can you use a battery and
some wires to light up two bulbs?
Ask a grown-up to help you.

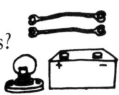

How are things turned off or on?

Science facts

If you put a switch into a circuit, you can turn a bulb, a motor or a buzzer on or off. When a switch is turned off, it breaks the circuit. When a switch is turned on, it completes the circuit. Things such as bulbs, motors and buzzers only work when a circuit is complete.

This is an open switch.
It is turned off.

This is a closed switch.
It is turned on.

Science quiz

Which of the circuits shown below will let the buzzer, bulb or motor work? Tick (✔) the right box.

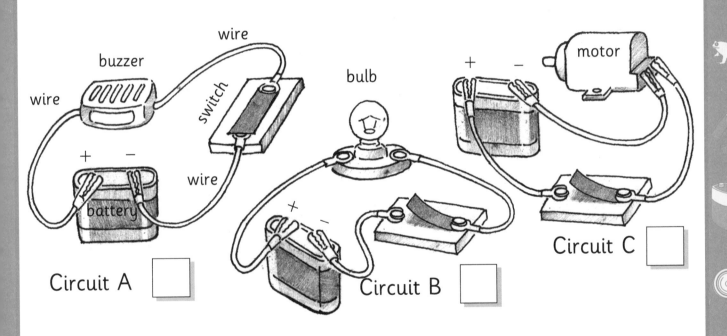

Circuit A

Circuit B

Circuit C

Science activity

Find out how turning a buzzer on and off can be used to send messages. Ask a grown-up to help you find this information. You may need to use reference books, CD-ROMs or the Internet.

How do things start and stop?

Science facts

Pushes and pulls are forces. When you push or pull something, you can make it start or stop moving.

Science quiz

Look at these pictures. Is the child in each one using a pushing force or a pulling force? Write **push** or **pull**. Does the force make a start or a stop? Write **start** or **stop**.

....

....

....

....

....

....

....

....

....

....

Science activity

Using a rope, play a game of tug of war with a friend. Can you make your friend start moving? Can you make your friend stop moving?

What makes things go faster?

Science facts

Pushes and pulls are forces that can make things move faster or slower. Pushes and pulls can also make things stop moving.

Science quiz

Can you answer these questions about making things move faster or slower?

How can Jason make the ball roll slower?

....

How can Amy make the ball move faster?

....

How can Luke make the bike go slower?

....

How can Anna make the ball move faster?

....

Science activity

Roll a marble through a cardboard tube. How can you use the tube to make the marble roll faster? How can you use it to make the marble roll slower?

Why do things change direction?

Science facts

Pushes and pulls are forces. Forces can make moving things change direction. If you blow at a table tennis ball that is rolling towards you, the ball will change direction. When you blow, your breath is the force pushing the ball.

Science quiz

Write **yes** or **no** beside each picture below to say whether or not the player is using a force that will make the ball change direction.

Science activity

Try to make a balloon change direction in midair by using a paper fan. There is one rule – you must never hit the balloon with the fan.

What makes a shadow?

Science facts

Light comes from different sources, such as the Sun, light bulbs and candles. When light shines on a wall, the ground or a piece of paper, it makes that thing look bright. When no light is shining, everything looks dark. By putting your hand between a light source and a surface, you can make a shadow. A shadow is a place where no light is shining.

Science quiz

Can you add the girl's shadow to this picture? Make sure it is in the right position.

Science activity

(!) Cut some shapes of people and animals out of cardboard. In a dark room, use your shapes and a torch to make a shadow-puppet show. What happens if you cut out the shapes from clear cling film?

What makes the sound change?

Science facts

A sound on a guitar is made by plucking a string. You can change the sound by changing the length of the string. Long strings make low notes; short strings make high notes. Other musical instruments work in similar ways.

Science quiz

Here are the wooden bars of a xylophone that has been taken apart. Number them in order from the lowest note to the highest note. Write **1** in the box below the lowest note and **8** below the highest.

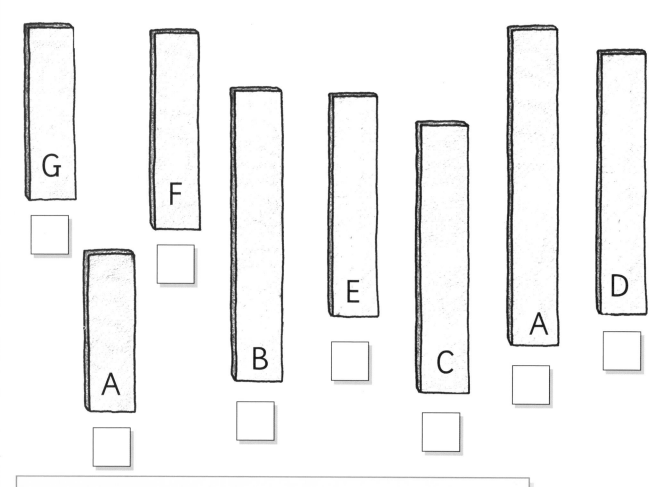

Science activity

Make a guitar from a box and some rubber bands. Can you make high and low sounds on your guitar? Can you make loud and soft sounds?

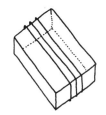

Can you hear it from far away?

Science facts

You use your ears to hear sounds. When a sound is near you, it can sound loud. When the same sound is far away, it will sound quieter.

Science quiz

Look at this picture. Sam is calling her friends to come inside and eat.

Which friend finds it the easiest to hear Sam calling?

....

Which friend finds it the hardest to hear her calling?

....

How can Sam make sure all her friends hear?

....

Science activity

Do you think it would be easier to hear quiet sounds if you had bigger ears? Ask a grown-up to help you make a cone from thin card. Hold the tapered end of the cone to your ear, and listen to faraway sounds. Do sounds seem louder with or without the cone?

What do these words mean?

Science facts

Scientists use special words. These words help them to write scientific information for others to read.

Science quiz

Can you remember what these words mean? Draw a line to join each scientific word with the phrase that describes it.

force	Describes things that grow and reproduce
animal	A push or pull that makes things move
alive	Something that turns a bulb, motor or buzzer on or off
plant	A living thing that moves around to find its food
switch	Materials that are not made in a factory
shadow	What living things use to know what is happening around them
senses	A place where animals and plants can be found
sound	A living thing that can make its own food
natural	Forms when something blocks out the light
circuit	Something that attracts metals such as iron
habitat	Describes what is made when things vibrate
magnet	Wires joined to a battery and a bulb, motor or buzzer

Science activity

Think about all the experiments and activities you carried out. How many times did you predict the correct answer? Were all the tests fair? If you repeated the experiments, would you do any of them differently?